JADED EYES

by Leila C. Edwards
illustrated by Diane Kidd

Harcourt
SCHOOL PUBLISHERS

Printed in China

ISBN 10: 0-15-351440-X
ISBN 13: 978-0-15-351440-1

Ordering Options
ISBN 10: 0-15-351213-X (Grade 3 Advanced Collection)
ISBN 13: 978-0-15-351213-1 (Grade 3 Advanced Collection)
ISBN 10: 0-15-358075-5 (package of 5)
ISBN 13: 978-0-15-358075-8 (package of 5)

4 5 6 7 8 9 10 0940 12 11 10 09

Jana had her great-grandmother's eyes.
At least, that's what she had always been told.
Sometimes she looked at the old photo of her
great-grandmother. Then she stared at herself
in the mirror.

Her father's eyes were blue. Her mother and
two brothers had brown eyes. Jana's eyes were
gray. She sometimes gave her father "the big
eyes" when she wanted something. He usually
smiled and said, "That won't work, Jana." Then,
sometimes, he let her
have her way.

Of course, Jana didn't think about her eyes most of the time. She thought of herself as just another person in third grade. She laughed with her friends, did her homework, and read before she went to bed. She adored reading. She wanted to be a school librarian like Mrs. Haines someday. Jana loved to spend time in the school library. Sometimes her teacher let her go there to help Mrs. Haines. From time to time, Jana was allowed to read stories to the first-graders.

One day, at an assembly in the gym, the principal announced that everyone would visit the school nurse for a vision check. Jana was the first to go in her class.

"I can't read that," Jana told the nurse.

"Try the one above, then," said Ms. Lesser.

"It's blurry, but it looks like K, O, V, T, E."

"Read the smallest row you can, Jana."

"I guess it's the second row: X, R, A, H, M."

The nurse smiled. "All right, Jana, you can go back to class now."

Later that day, Jana laughed with her friend Halle. "That eye test was really hard," she said.

"I thought it was actually pretty easy," Halle replied.

A few days later, a note for Jana's parents was in her homework folder.

"It seems that you didn't do so well on the eye test," her father said calmly. "It says you should see an eye doctor for a full exam."

"I can see fine!" Jana insisted.

"Still," her father said, "we need to be sure."

"That silly test at school was wrong," Jana murmured.

At the eye doctor's office, Jana took plenty of time as she looked through a machine at letters on a screen.

"She has healthy eyes, but she does need to wear glasses," the doctor said. "Ms. Thomas will help you select a pair of frames, Jana. It was nice to meet you."

While Ms. Thomas was helping someone else, Jana whispered to her mother, "I don't want glasses, and I don't need them."

"Well, the doctor says you do need them. You can't just dismiss the truth," her mother said.

Jana didn't like any of the frames. She squirmed and took a very long time to pick one. When she finally chose a frame, Ms. Thomas and her mother said it went perfectly with the shape of her face.

On the way home, Jana pictured her friends making fun of her. She thought of the horrible names they might call her.

"I really don't think that will happen," her mother said gently. "Do you call people names who wear glasses?"

"No, but this is different because, well, because it's me!" said Jana.

The next day, Jana and her mom went to pick up the glasses. Jana dreaded getting them. When she put the glasses on, though, she was amazed at how well she could see. Even so, they felt strange at first.

"It will take about an hour to get used to them," Ms. Thomas said.

Jana saw a totally different world on the way home. Things that had been a patchwork of shapes and colors were now sharp and clear. By bedtime, Jana forgot she was wearing the glasses.

She remembered the next morning. It was Saturday and there was no school. She left the glasses on her dresser and hurried down to breakfast.

"Where are your glasses, Jana?" her mom wanted to know.

"I don't have to wear them on the weekends," she answered.

"You have to wear them every day. Please go get them," said her father firmly.

"Maybe my eyes will get stronger if I don't wear them," declared Jana.

"Jana, go put on your glasses," her father said.

Later that day, Jana and her father went grocery shopping. As they turned the cart up the produce aisle, Jana looked up in surprise. There was Mrs. Haines from the school library!

"I don't want anyone to see me," thought Jana anxiously.

Suddenly, Mrs. Haines turned around. Jana got a second shock because Mrs. Haines was wearing glasses, too!

"Hi, Mrs. Haines." Jana didn't know what to say.

Mrs. Haines smiled and said, "I guess you notice something different about me. I just got them yesterday."

"As we get older," Mrs. Haines said, "our eyes change. I can't see things close up as well as I would like."

"I can't see things that are far away," Jana said.

"I guess we're in the same club," Mrs. Haines laughed. "I hope mine look half as cool as yours," said Mrs. Haines.

Jana felt better about her glasses after speaking with Mrs. Haines. She ended up wearing them all weekend.

When Monday morning came, Jana wondered what her friends would say.

"Hey, you got glasses, and they're really cute!" Halle announced.

Mike came over, stared at her, and asked, "What's different about you?"

"Very funny," Jana replied sarcastically.

"Welcome to the club," Mike grinned, pointing to his glasses. He took his autographed football from his backpack. "Go out for a pass and maybe now you can actually see it."

Jana slowly got used to her glasses. She could see the board in class more easily. She noticed more around her. She spotted things more quickly. When she helped Mrs. Haines in the library, Jana could pick out book titles much faster.

Her glasses steamed up when she came in from the cold, and she had to keep them clean. Everywhere she went, though, she could see things she had never seen before. "My eyes may look like my great-grandmother's," Jana thought, "but I'm happy these eyes are all mine!"

Think Critically

1. How many people are in Jana's family and what color are their eyes?

2. What details does the author give about eye testing?

3. Why is Jana so upset by the idea of getting glasses?

4. How would you describe Jana's father?

5. How would you have felt about getting glasses if you had been Jana?

⭐ Language Arts

Write a Poem Pretend that you are Jana and that you just got your new glasses. Write a poem about how your world changed.

 School-Home Connection How many people do you know who wear glasses? Talk to friends and family members who do. Find out how long they have worn them, how they found out they needed them, and what they thought about them.

Word Count: 1,017